This book belongs to

....

The Time Capsule
and Other Stories

How this collection works

This *Biff, Chip and Kipper* collection is one of a series of four books at **Read with Oxford Stage 4**. It contains four stories: *Land of Letters*, *Paris Adventure*, *The Time Capsule* and *The Jigsaw Puzzle*. These stories will help to broaden your child's wider reading experience. There are also fun activities to enjoy throughout the book.

How to use this book

Find a time to read with your child when they are not too tired and are happy to concentrate for about fifteen to twenty minutes. Reading with your child should be a shared and enjoyable experience. It is best to choose just one of the stories for each session.

For each story, there are tips for reading the story together. At the end of the story you will find four 'Talk about the story' questions. These will help your child to think about what they have read, and to relate the story to their own experiences. The questions are followed by a fun activity.

Enjoy sharing the stories!

Contents

OXFORD
UNIVERSITY PRESS

Authors and illustrators

Land of Letters written by Paul Shipton, illustrated by Alex Brychta

Paris Adventure written by Roderick Hunt, illustrated by Alex Brychta

The Time Capsule written by Paul Shipton, illustrated by Alex Brychta

The Jigsaw Puzzle written by Roderick Hunt, illustrated by Alex Brychta

OXFORD
UNIVERSITY PRESS

Great Clarendon Street, Oxford, OX2 6DP, United Kingdom

Oxford University Press is a department of the University
of Oxford. It furthers the University's objective of excellence
in research, scholarship, and education by publishing
worldwide. Oxford is a registered trade mark of Oxford
University Press in the UK and in certain other countries

The Jigsaw Puzzle first published in 1994
Paris Adventure first published in 2007
Land of Letters, The Time Capsule first published in 2015
This Edition published in 2018

British Library Cataloguing in Publication Data
Data available

ISBN: 978-0-19-276429-4

10 9 8 7 6 5 4 3

Paper used in the production of this book is a natural, recyclable product
made from wood grown in sustainable forests. The manufacturing process
conforms to the environmental regulations of the country of origin.

Printed in China

Acknowledgements

Series Editor: Annemarie Young
Additional artwork by Stuart Trotter

Tips for reading *Land of Letters*

Children learn best when reading is relaxed and enjoyable.

- Talk about the title and the picture on page 6. Then read the speech bubble.

- Discuss what you think the story might be about.

- Share the story, encouraging your child to read as much of it as they can.

- Give lots of praise as your child reads, and help them when necessary.

- If your child gets stuck on a word that is decodable, encourage them to say the sounds and then blend them together to read the word. Read the whole sentence again. Focus on the meaning.

- If the word is not decodable, or is still too tricky, just read the word for them, re-read the sentence and move on.

- When you've finished reading the story, talk about it with your child, using the 'Talk about the story' questions at the end. Then do the activity.

Children enjoy re-reading stories, and this helps to build their confidence.

Have fun!

 For more activities, free eBooks and practical advice to help your child progress with reading visit **oxfordowl.co.uk**

Land of Letters

The magic key takes the children to a world with letters everywhere!

Kipper was writing a story.

"Will you check the spelling for me?" he asked Biff.

"There is no letter 'j' in 'orange'," Biff said.

"You spell 'orange' with a 'g' and an 'e' at the end," added Chip.

The magic key began to glow. It was time for an
adventure.

"I want to write my story!" said Kipper.

The magic took them to a very strange place.

Kipper looked around. "Where are we?" he asked.

"There are letters everywhere!"

There were letters on the ground and letters in the air.

"It's a world of letters!" said Biff.

Some letters were floating high in the sky. With a flash they joined together to make the word 'cloud'. Then they *became* a cloud.

"I've got an idea!" said Biff. Quickly she collected some letters on the ground. She started to spell a word.

Biff spelled the word 'snack'.

There was another flash of light and the letters on the ground became a snack.

Biff picked up the letter 'c' and pulled a bit off
the corner.

"Yum!" she said. "Try some of this. It's cake!"

A letter 'e' floated down from the sky and joined the letters on the ground.

It made a new word. The word was 'snake'.

There was a flash of light.

Then the letters became a snake. A *big* snake.

It gave the children a hungry glare.

"Run!" shouted Kipper.

The children started to run away.

The huge snake followed them with a hiss.

"I'm not sure I like this place!" said Kipper.

"Where's the magic key?" Chip shouted to Biff.

"We need to go!"

Biff looked in her pockets but the magic key was not there.

"I haven't got it," she cried. "Where can it be?"

Chip was picking up more letters from the ground.
He pushed a 'k', an 'e' and a 'y' together to spell 'key'.

The letters became a real key but it was not the
right key.

"That won't work!" said Biff. "It's not the
magic key."

Chip looked around for more letters.

"I think we need to spell the words 'magic key'," he said.

Soon Chip had all the letters except one.
"Can you see a 'g'?" he asked.

Kipper turned round. Then he ran in the direction of the huge snake. He had to dodge around it.

"Be careful!" shouted Biff.

Then Kipper reached up. He grabbed an orange from a branch on the tree behind the snake.

He pulled the orange apart.

"It's made of all the letters to spell 'orange'!" he said.

Kipper pulled out the letter 'g' and threw it to Chip.
"Now you can spell 'magic key'," he shouted.

With a flash, the words on the ground became the real magic key.

It started to glow.

"We're going home!" cried Chip.

At home Kipper looked at his notebook.

"I've got a new story to write," he said.

"And now you can spell 'orange'!" said Biff.

Talk about the story

What do you think gave Biff the idea of spelling the word 'snack'?

What made the snack turn into a snake?

What made Kipper pick the orange?

What word would you spell out in the land of letters?

31

Find the country

Which letter is in the names of all the countries except one? Which country name doesn't contain that letter?

Mexico

Spain

Russia

Australia

Egypt

India

Tips for reading *Paris Adventure*

Children learn best when reading is relaxed and enjoyable.

- Talk about the title and the picture on page 34. Then read the speech bubble.

- Discuss what you think the story might be about.

- Share the story, encouraging your child to read as much of it as they can.

- Give lots of praise as your child reads, and help them when necessary.

- If your child gets stuck on a word that is decodable, encourage them to say the sounds and then blend them together to read the word. Read the whole sentence again. Focus on the meaning.

- If the word is not decodable, or is still too tricky, just read the word for them, re-read the sentence and move on.

- When you've finished reading the story, talk about it with your child, using the 'Talk about the story' questions at the end. Then do the activity.

Children enjoy re-reading stories, and this helps to build their confidence.

Have fun!

For more activities, free eBooks and practical advice to help your child progress with reading visit **oxfordowl.co.uk**

Paris Adventure

The magic key takes the children to Paris. Why can't they find the Eiffel Tower?

The children were doing a project on France.
Mrs May showed them some pictures of Paris.

Mrs May showed them a picture of the Eiffel Tower.

"It looks very tall," said Biff.

After school Mum came to meet Biff and Chip. Biff had a picture of Paris.

"We are doing a project on France," she said.

Later Nadim and Anneena came to play with Biff
and Chip. Anneena had a model of the Eiffel Tower.

"I know," said Chip. "Let's paint the French flag."

He got a big sheet of paper and they began to paint it.

Suddenly the magic key began to glow. It was time for an adventure.

"Oh no!" said Biff. "I wanted to finish painting the flag."

The magic took them back in time. It took them to
a busy town.

"There are no cars," said Chip. "This must be a
long time ago."

"I know where we are," said Biff.

"We are in Paris. Look at all the flags."

Anneena was excited. "We can go and see the Eiffel Tower," she said.

The children looked for the Eiffel Tower but
they couldn't find it.

"Are you sure this is Paris?" asked Chip.

Nadim asked a policeman. "Do you know where
the Eiffel Tower is?" he asked.

"The Eiffel Tower!" said the policeman.

"There is no such thing."

Anneena asked a lady. "Do you know
where the Eiffel Tower is?" she asked.

"The Eiffel Tower!" said the lady. "There is no
such thing."

"I know why we can't find the Eiffel Tower,"
said Biff. "It hasn't been invented."

Just then they saw a man. He was pulling a cart.

"Will you help?" asked the man. "I can't get the cart up this step."

The children helped the man pull the cart into a hall.

The man pulled a sheet off the cart. "This is my model," he said.

"What is it?" asked Nadim.

"It is a torch," said the man. "It will be taller than all the houses in Paris. People will see it for miles. Here is a picture. It will look like this."

The children looked round the hall. There were lots
of models.

"It's a competition," said Chip. "I know which one
will win ... the Eiffel Tower!"

"But I can't see the Eiffel Tower," said Nadim.

Some people began to look at the models to see which was the best.

"Everyone will see my torch for miles," said the
man. "At night the top will light up like this!" He
plugged in the torch.

There was a loud bang. The top of the torch blew
off. Then it fell over with a crash.

"Ah!" said the man. "It needs a little work."

Anneena had an idea. She began to lift the broken torch.

"Help me, everyone," she said.

The children turned the torch upside down.
"What does it look like to you?" asked Anneena.

"It looks like the Eiffel Tower," said Biff. She spoke
to the man.

"Excuse me," she said. "Why not make the torch
into a tower?"

"Excuse me," said Anneena. But is your name
Eiffel?"

"Brilliant!" said the man. "Brilliant!" Just then
the magic key began to glow.

"I wonder if that was Monsieur Eiffel," said Biff.

"And if that was how the Eiffel Tower was invented!" said Nadim.

Talk about the story

Why did Chip say "it must be a long time ago"?

Why couldn't the children find the Eiffel Tower?

Why wasn't Monsieur Eiffel's torch idea a good one?

What would you like to build for your town?

Find the destinations

The magic key is taking the children to different places
– Paris, London and New York. Follow the instructions
to find out who is going where.

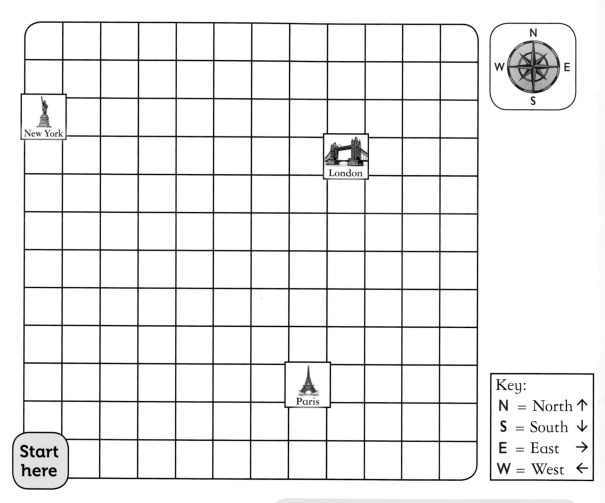

To find the destinations,
use the key to move the
right number of squares.

Instructions

Biff: E-4, N-7, E-6, S-5, W-3

Chip: N-3, E-9, N-6, W-1, S-1

Kipper: E-5, N-7, W-4, N-2, W-1

Tips for reading *The Time Capsule*

Children learn best when reading is relaxed and enjoyable.

- Talk about the title and the picture on page 62. Then read the speech bubble.

- Discuss what you think the story might be about.

- Share the story, encouraging your child to read as much of it as they can.

- Give lots of praise as your child reads, and help them when necessary.

- If your child gets stuck on a word that is decodable, encourage them to say the sounds and then blend them together to read the word. Read the whole sentence again. Focus on the meaning.

- If the word is not decodable, or is still too tricky, just read the word for them, re-read the sentence and move on.

- When you've finished reading the story, talk about it with your child, using the 'Talk about the story' questions at the end. Then do the activity.

- Re-read the story later, again encouraging your child to read as much of it as they can.

Children enjoy re-reading stories, and this helps to build their confidence.

Have fun!

 For more activities, free eBooks and practical advice to help your child progress with reading visit **oxfordowl.co.uk**

The Time Capsule

What will the children put in their time capsule?

Biff and Chip were going to the swimming pool with Mum.

"Can we go past the school?" asked Biff. "They're building a new classroom. Perhaps we'll see the digger!"

Nobody was working the digger. The builders
were all looking down into a hole.

"I think they've found something," said Chip.

One builder jumped into the hole with a spade.
A moment later he lifted something up.

"It looks like a metal box," said Biff. "I wonder what's in it."

"There might be treasure inside it!" said Chip.
"Perhaps robbers hid their loot underground!"

"You never know," said Mum. "You'll have to
ask your teacher about it on Monday."

Biff and Chip didn't have to ask about the box on Monday because Mrs May was waiting to tell the class about it.

"The builders found something very interesting this weekend," she said.

Mrs May opened the lid and took out a letter.

"Hello, people of the future," she read aloud.
"Inside this box you will find things that tell you
all about life in our time."

"This box is a time capsule," explained Mrs May.
"Some children at our school made it years ago. They
buried it so people wouldn't find it for a long time."

Inside the box there was a scrapbook with lots of photos.

"Look how old-fashioned the cars and clothes are," said Nadim.

There were plastic toys, sweet wrappers, comics
and newspapers in the box, too.

"Look at this old newspaper," said Biff.

"This time capsule was made before your mums and dads were born," said Mrs May.

"Wow," said Chip. "So when the children buried it, _we_ were the 'people of the future'!"

After school, Biff and Chip told the family all
about the time capsule.

"Can *we* make a time capsule and bury it in the
garden?" asked Chip.

"That's a great idea!" said Mum.

Dad went to find a strong container.

Mum asked the children what they wanted to put in the time capsule.

"I want to write a letter telling people all about my hobbies," said Biff.

She went and got a shell from her shell collection to go with her letter.

Kipper was looking at the family photos.

"I want a photo of me and Lee to put in the time capsule," he said.

"I'd like to tell the people of the future about how we live today," said Chip.

"Why not use our camera?" said Mum.

"Great!" said Chip. "Then I can *show* them how we live!"

Mum showed Chip how to film using the camera.

"What shall I film?" asked Chip.

"Try and show things that people in the future might not know about," said Mum.

"I know! Biff, I'll film you playing football,"
said Chip. "In the future, sports might be
completely different."

They went outside with Biff's football.

Biff kicked the ball up once, twice . . . On the third kick the ball got stuck in a tree.

Chip turned off the camera. "I don't think the people of the future will want to see that," he said.

Chip went to find Kipper.

"I'll film you getting Floppy to do his tricks," said Chip. "In the future, people might have different kinds of pets."

"OK," said Chip. "I'm filming now."

"Sit, Floppy," said Kipper. Floppy looked up at Kipper, but he didn't sit. Then he ran away. Chip turned off the camera and sighed.

Chip took the camera inside.

"I'll film Dad making dinner," he said. "In the future meals might be completely different."

Chip pointed the camera at Dad.

"Tell us what you're making," he said.

"Not now, Chip!" cried Dad. "I left dinner in the oven too long. It's burning!"

Smoke was coming from the oven.

Dad opened a window to let all the smoke out.
A football flew in through the open window and
hit him.

"Sorry!" shouted Biff from outside.

Chip pushed the off button again.

When Mum saw what had happened, she said, "I'll cycle into town for a takeaway."

"I'll film you riding off," said Chip. "People in the future may not have bikes."

Outside Mum checked her bike. "Sorry, Chip. I'm afraid you can't film my bike. I've got a puncture."

Before Chip turned the camera off again, Floppy ran around the corner.

Kipper ran after him shouting, "Come back!"
He chased Floppy in circles round and round Mum.
    "What will people in the future make of this?"
said Chip, turning the camera off.

Later the family all watched Chip's film on the computer. They laughed at Kipper and Floppy's tricks. They laughed when Biff's football got Dad's shirt muddy.

Only Chip was quiet.

"Everything went wrong," he said. "I wanted to show the people of the future about life in our time."

"You have!" said Mum. "Your film shows life in *our* family perfectly!"

The children put a disc with Chip's film into the
box with everything else. They closed the box and
sealed it up with tape.

Mum wrote the date on the outside of the capsule.

The children put the time capsule into a hole that
Dad had dug in the garden.

"I wonder who will find it," said Biff.

Dad started to fill in the hole.

"I wonder *when* anyone will find our time capsule,"
said Chip. "It may be hundreds of years from now."

"It might not be quite so long," said Mum.

She pointed outside. "Floppy's just dug up your time capsule!"

Floppy had the time capsule in his mouth. He was pulling it out of the hole.

Kipper ran to the garden. "Floppy, drop it!"
he shouted.

"Quick Chip, get the camera," said Dad. "I'm
sure the people of the future will want to see this!"

Talk about the story

What were the diggers doing at the school?

What did Biff, Chip and Kipper want to put into their time capsule?

What did Mum think of Chip's film?

What would you put in a time capsule?

Memory game

Look at the things from another time capsule for a minute,
then look away and see how many you can remember.
Ask an adult to write down the things you remember.

Tips for reading *The Jigsaw Puzzle*

Children learn best when reading is relaxed and enjoyable.

- Talk about the title and the picture on page 98. Then read the speech bubble.

- Discuss what you think the story might be about.

- Share the story, encouraging your child to read as much of it as they can.

- Give lots of praise as your child reads, and help them when necessary.

- If your child gets stuck on a word that is decodable, encourage them to say the sounds and then blend them together to read the word. Read the whole sentence again. Focus on the meaning.

- If the word is not decodable, or is still too tricky, just read the word for them, re-read the sentence and move on.

- When you've finished reading the story, talk about it with your child, using the 'Talk about the story' questions at the end. Then do the activity.

Children enjoy re-reading stories, and this helps to build their confidence.

Have fun!

 For more activities, free eBooks and practical advice to help your child progress with reading visit **oxfordowl.co.uk**

The Jigsaw Puzzle

What happens when the children's jigsaw puzzle takes them into the past?

It was raining. The children were fed up. Biff
and Anneena were bored, and Chip was in a bad
mood. He wanted to play with the frisbee.

Mum had an idea. She had a new jigsaw puzzle. She gave it to the children.

"You can do this jigsaw," she said. "It's a good one."

Everyone looked at the jigsaw. It was a picture of
soldiers and a boy.

"The soldiers are asking the boy a question," said
Mum. "They want to know where his father is."

The jigsaw puzzle had lots of pieces. The children
liked the jigsaw, but it was hard to do. Soon, Chip
got bored with it. He began to play with the frisbee.

In the end, everyone got bored. The magic key
began to glow. The magic took the children into a
new adventure.

The magic took the children to a time long ago.
It took them to a big house. Some children were
playing with their mother and father.

Kipper looked at the children.

"What funny clothes they're wearing," he said.

"They look like the children in the picture on the jigsaw," said Anneena.

Kipper spoke to the girl and boy.

"Hello," he said "My name's Kipper. This is Biff, Chip and Anneena."

"What funny names!" said the girl. "And what funny clothes you're wearing."

"What are your names?" asked Chip.

"My name is Jane," said the girl.

"My name is Edmund," said the boy, "and my father is very important."

"We don't mind," said Kipper.

Edmund had never seen a frisbee before.

"Why have you got a plate?" he asked.

"It's not a plate," said Kipper. "It's a frisbee."

Everyone played with it.

Suddenly, there was a shout. A man ran towards
Edmund's father.

"Quickly, you must hide!" he said. "Get inside the
house. The soldiers are coming!"

Edmund's father ran inside.

"Quickly!" shouted Edmund. "We must help my father to hide. The soldiers mustn't find him."

Everyone ran into the house.

The soldiers came to the house. They knocked on
the door.

"Let us in!" they shouted. "Open the door, or we'll
smash it down."

Everyone ran to the library. The library had
a secret room. The room was behind a bookcase.
Edmund's father hid in the secret room.

"Good luck, Father," said Edmund.

Edmund's mother pushed the bookcase back.

"Don't tell the soldiers about the secret room," said Jane. "They will kill my father if they find him."

The soldiers ran into the house. They looked for
Edmund's father.

"Tell us where he is!" they shouted.

The children were frightened, but they didn't
say anything.

The soldiers looked everywhere, but they couldn't find Edmund's father. One of the soldiers found a sword.

"His sword is here," he said, "so he must be here somewhere."

The soldiers took everyone into a room. Some
men sat at a big table. They looked at the
children. One of them looked at Kipper.

"Come here, little boy," he said.

"Where is your father?" asked the man.
Kipper was frightened, but he didn't say
anything. None of the children said anything.

The important men were angry.

"Your father is hiding," they shouted. "Tell us where he is. If he is hiding in this house, we will soon find him."

Nobody said anything, so the soldiers began
to pull up the floor. They tapped on the walls.
Edmund's mother was frightened.

"They may find him," she said.

Edmund and Jane were frightened. They wanted
to help their father. Suddenly, Chip had an idea.

"Maybe your father could escape, if he dressed up
as a woman," he said.

Biff and Anneena had an idea too. Biff threw
the frisbee at a soldier. The soldier laughed. He
had never seen a frisbee before.

"Come and look at this!" he shouted.

The soldiers wanted a rest, so they stopped looking for Edmund's father. They all went outside and played with the frisbee. Soon, everyone was laughing.

The soldiers liked the frisbee. They played with
it for a long time. Suddenly, an old woman came
up. She looked very poor. She wanted some money.

The soldiers stopped playing with the frisbee.
They shouted at the old woman.

"Go away!" they shouted. "We don't have
any money."

Suddenly, one of the soldiers looked at the house.
He saw someone running away.

"Look! Over there!" he shouted. "Someone's
running away."

The soldiers chased the woman.

"It's not a woman, it's a man," they shouted. "It must be the man we want. Don't let him get away."

The soldiers caught the man and took him back
to the house.

"Oh no!" said Anneena. "They've caught
Edmund's father. Our idea didn't work."

The soldiers thought they had caught Edmund's father. But it was a trick.

"Grrr!" said the soldiers.

"Hooray!" said the children.

The children found some old clothes.

"So Edmund's father was the old woman,"
said Anneena.

"What a good trick," laughed everyone.

Suddenly, the magic key began to glow.

The jigsaw puzzle was finished. Mum looked at something in the picture.

"That's funny," she said. "That looks like a frisbee."

"It must be a plate," said Chip.

Talk about the story

Why did the soldier say Edmund's father must be in the house?

Where did the soldiers look?

How did Edmund's father escape?

What's your best hiding place?

Find the words

Search for eight words from the story in the puzzle.

clothes   escape   frisbee   key
plate   puzzle   soldier   sword

T	S	I	C	K	R	O	S
R	O	P	L	A	T	E	W
Y	L	U	O	S	H	S	O
Z	D	J	T	P	S	C	R
P	I	X	H	I	D	A	D
K	E	Y	E	C	Y	P	J
F	R	I	S	B	E	E	A
B	O	P	U	Z	Z	L	E
C	M	N	I	H	M	T	W

Remembering the stories together

Encourage your child to remember and retell the stories in this book. You could ask questions like these:

- Who are the characters in the story?

- What happens at the beginning of the story?

- What happens next?

- How does the story end?

- What was your favourite part of the story? Why?

Story prompts

When talking to your child about the stories, you could use these more detailed reminders to help them remember the exact sequence of events. Turn the statements below into questions, so that your child can give you the answers. For example, *Where does the magic key take the children? What happens when the children eat the letter 'c'?* And so on …

Land of Letters

- The magic key takes the children to a world made of letters.

- When the children eat the letter 'c' from the word 'snack', an 'e' joins the letters and becomes a snake!

- They can't find the magic key to get home, so they spell the word 'key'.

- It doesn't become the right key, so they try to spell 'magic key', but can't find a 'g'. Kipper picks an orange off the tree and finds all the letters to spell 'orange' inside it.

- They use the 'g' to the make the word 'magic'. It becomes the magic key and takes them home.

Paris Adventure

- The children are doing a school project on France.

- The magic key takes them to Paris before the Eiffel Tower was built.

- They discover a model of a torch which is part of a competition.

- The children suggest that the model would be better the other way up as a tower - The Eiffel Tower!

- The magic key takes them home.

The Time Capsule

- Mum and the children see builders at the school, digging up the playground.

- The builders find a time capsule with lots of things from the past.

- The children decide to make their own time capsule for future children.

- Chip tries to make a video, but everything keeps going wrong.

- They decide to include the video anyway, as it shows their life as it is – chaotic!

- When they bury the time capsule in the garden, Floppy digs it up and runs off with it.

The Jigsaw Puzzle

- On a rainy day, Mum suggests doing a jigsaw instead of playing frisbee, but the magic key takes them on an adventure into the jigsaw.

- Soldiers arrive, looking for Edmund's father, and the children help hide him in a secret room.

- Then Chip has an idea – to dress Edmund's father up as a woman to escape.

- Biff distracts the soldiers with the frisbee, whilst Edmund's father escapes dressed as a woman.

- The soldiers see a woman running off and capture her thinking she is Edmund's father, but it is all a trick!

- At home they notice that the jigsaw now has a frisbee in it.

You could now encourage your child to create a 'story map' of each story, drawing and colouring all the key parts of them. This will help them identify the main elements of the stories and learn to create their own stories.